WEST C
WEATH GUIDE

C000216640

Craig Rich

Contents

Keeping in touch with the nerve centre of weather forecasting in the south – west. Craig is a regular visitor to the Met. Office at RAF Mount Batten which supplies the information needed for the daily forecast in *Spotlight South West*.

1   The south-west region

The combination of superb sandy beaches, magnificent scenic coastal footpaths, craggy moorlands and historic buildings provides wide and varied points of interest for the holiday-maker, but the counties of Cornwall, Devon, parts of Somerset and Dorset which make up the region are famous not only for their holiday and tourist attractions but also for the variations in weather both from season to season and from day to day. It is a region that can be almost sub-tropical in the summer, evidenced by the abundance of palm trees in the southern coastal resorts, yet at the same time reel under the ferocity of an Atlantic storm such as that which decimated the Fastnet yacht race fleet in 1979. While daffodils bloom in mid-winter in the Isles of Scilly, Dartmoor and Exmoor have suffered some of the most severe blizzards on record. Floods due to rain-water pouring off the moors and causing the rivers to rise and overflow their banks have also resulted in disasters, such as that at Lynmouth in 1952. A little knowledge of the region's climate, and of the weather conditions to be expected, is invaluable to the holiday-maker, the local inhabitant and anyone (such as those about to retire) thinking of coming to live in the area.

The south-west is also renowned for its traffic jams in the high season and yet with just a little knowledge of the time of season and likely weather conditions it is possible to enjoy its beaches, towns and countryside with a minimum of frustration.

School holidays are obviously the busiest periods with the peak fortnight occurring at the end of July and beginning of August when accommodation is at its most expensive and most difficult to find and when car-parks, cafes, beaches and other public places are most crowded. Later in August, though, there is a noticeable reduction in pressure and since the switch of the August Bank Holiday to the end of the month the week preceding it has become the quietest in the school-holiday period.

The beginning and end of the season are particularly suitable times to head for the West Country for short 'mini-breaks'. Apart from the relative quiet, accommodation is readily available without the need to book and the high speed train and M4/M5 motorways make access relatively quick and easy. Perhaps the most satisfied visitors are those who come at short notice during a spell of fine weather and are able to take advantage of the very attractive off-season package rates offered by many hotels between October (including the autumn half-term period) and April. The English Tourist Board (4 Grosvenor Gardens, London, SW1W 0DU) publishes annually a booklet entitled, *Let's Go: Short breaks in autumn, winter and spring*. It contains much useful information on the region and is well worth obtaining. Even in winter, the mild sunny weather frequently enjoyed in the south-west while many parts of the country are suffering sub-zero temperatures makes it ideal for a 'break'.

Most people, however, have to take their holidays in the summer when Saturday-to-Saturday bookings are the norm in most camp-sites, hotels and boarding houses. Travelling mid-week, or even on Friday, though, is a considerable advantage and the worst traffic can be avoided. On the busiest Saturdays, for example, such is the congestion on the M5 that the police have to prevent motorists from queuing for petrol on the motorway itself because the service areas are crammed to capacity. Delays such as these can be as tiring and frustrating in hot, dry weather as when it is raining. Furthermore, such an experience either at the beginning or the end of a holiday can spoil the fun.

If travelling on a Saturday is essential, then avoiding driving into the region between 8am and 4pm, and out of the region between 9am and lunch-time, will diminish the chance of long delays. Fortunately this only applies on the busiest July and August Saturdays. When it is wet on Friday, especially if the rest of the holiday period has been fine, many people leave early to 'beat the jams' and for this reason Fridays are occasionally actually busier than Saturdays.

There are a few general points about the region which are worth remembering. First, certain kinds of weather will cause conditions to differ dramatically on the north and south coasts, and on the moors and lower-lying ground. (Ever-more visitors drive from coast to coast across the region to catch the sunshine, particularly in Cornwall where the peninsula is very narrow and the distance involved is small.) Second, wet weather prevents people settling on the beach and results in heavier traffic on the roads. Congestion is

A typical Dartmoor scene with the familiar ponies and rocky skyline. The statocumulus clouds above point to stable air and good flying conditions above the cloud; turbulence below it. (West Country Tourist Board)

especially bad when it rains after a few fine days and thousands of visitors decide that after several days on the beach it is time to explore further afield and cool the sunburn!

Wednesdays (market day) are generally the busiest in Newton Abbot, Thursdays in Plymouth and Fridays (market day) in Barnstaple, to name three Devon examples, but congestion is always greater if it is unsettled non-beach weather, and really bad when it rains after a fine start to the week. Most people tend to spend their first few days at anchor, Mondays and Tuesdays being the busiest beach days — weather permitting. Exploring further afield early in the week, therefore, often avoids the worst congestion. Beaches are usually quieter on Fridays and Saturdays when most people are travelling into or out of the region.

The moors — especially Dartmoor — are not particularly popular in fine weather during the peak season when most holiday-makers and family parties spend their time on the beach. Relative seclusion, therefore, can be found in late July and early August away from the coast. Dartmoor is especially popular in September when most children have returned to school and tourists are mainly adults. Fine weather at the beginning and end of the season draws many people to the moors when, despite the good weather, the beaches are rather chilly. It must be remembered, though, that many people entering and leaving the region on Saturday cross the moors en route.

There is a final general point regarding weather which is worth mentioning here. It is that sustained sunny weather is often accompanied by a haze which can spoil some of the moorland views. Many of the best photographs, therefore, are taken in the clear weather following a rainstorm when dust particles in the atmosphere are few.

The inhabitants of the south-west have come to know the combined effect (such as traffic congestion) of the time of season and the weather. Asked at a convenient time they usually enjoy passing on this knowledge to visitors.

This book includes mention of most of the best-known places in the region, but the author has followed his own taste and chosen those which are favourites of his — the book does not claim to be a totally comprehensive guide and, inevitably, some favourites of other people will have been left out.

2   The vagaries of the weather

The geography of the south-west is very varied and perhaps a convenient starting point is the solid backbone of the region: Dartmoor and Bodmin Moor are predominantly granite, for which the area is famous, and many houses in Devon and Cornwall are built of the stone. Exmoor consists of sandstone and shale but its highest point, Dunkery Beacon at 520m (1,706ft) above sea-level, is some 98m (322ft) below the highest point of Dartmoor, High Willhays, at 618m (2,028ft). Bodmin Moor is much smaller in area than Dartmoor or Exmoor and rises to a maximum height of 419m (1,375ft) at Brown Willy. Other upland areas are located: on the East Devon, Somerset and Dorset borders north of Sidmouth where the Blackdown Hills are 315m (1,035ft) at their highest; at Hensbarrow Down in the heart of the St Austell China Clay Pits, which has a high point of 311m (1,020ft); at Carmenellis between Redruth and Helston with a maximum height of 250m (819ft); and in the Penwith area around Land's End most of which is above 183m (600ft), its highest points being Trendrine Hill and Watch Croft, both over 244m (800ft).

The climate is subject to a strong maritime influence, because of the narrowness of the peninsula and the way in which it thrusts out into the Atlantic to within a few miles of the southward-flowing remnants of the warm current which starts life as the Gulf Stream.

This maritime influence results in very mild weather in comparison with other parts of the country. The vegetation, consequently, is unique in the United Kingdom with palm-trees flourishing in the southern coastal areas of Penzance, Falmouth and Torbay. Despite the growth of sub-tropical trees in the sheltered coastal areas, however, away from these areas the growth of trees has been severely limited by the gales of the winter and — occasionally — summer months. This suggests wide-ranging variations in the weather across the region and, apart from the presence of the sea, it is largely the topography of the area which causes these variations.

Both Dartmoor and Exmoor form the cores of national parks; the Dartmoor national park covering 365 square miles of South Devon and the Exmoor national park covering 77 square miles along the northern coasts of Devon and Somerset. Both the northern and southern plateaux of Dartmoor above 366m (1,200ft) have large areas of blanket bog while the remainder above 305m (1,000ft) is covered mainly by common heather. The high rainfall and blanket bogs of the higher moors are the main reason for the desolation and lack of habitation on Dartmoor. To the walker, these conditions become even more of a hazard when the moors are shrouded in low cloud, and are widely held as the main reason for the few escapes from the notorious prison.

Exmoor is a fine example of the way in which even places near to each other can have different climates. Rainfall on the coast, for instance, is only about half that on the moors, and although snow can lie on the moors for long periods, as it did on Exmoor early in 1979 when so many sheep perished, it very rarely settles on the

Frontal clearance. And suddenly the rain stops; frequent sight on the West of England peninsula on the clearance of a warm front. (R.K. Pilsbury)

One of the latest electronic aids to forecasting in the south - west. The Principal Meteorological Officer in Plymouth, Mr Norman Hormbrey, shows Craig the read-out from a special radar station at Camborne. The station looks out to the Atlantic and picks up rain and storms approaching the region.

coast. Comparing Hawkridge on Exmoor at 314m (1,030ft) with Hartland Point on the coast at 91m (299ft), we find that on average Hawkridge has 1,526mm (about 60in) of rain a year compared with Hartland's 866mm (about 34in). Hartland has 1,640 hours of sunshine per year against Hawkridge's 1,403 hours. Hawkridge has ground frost on 109 days in the year against Hartland's 27 days and the extreme maximum temperature at Hawkridge is 25.6°C (78.1°F) compared to Hartland's 31.1°C (88°F).

There are variations between coastal observations and, once again using the Hartland statistics but comparing them this time with Plymouth which is almost due south but on the opposite coast, we find that although average and extreme temperatures for the year are remarkably similar, in the summer months Plymouth is, on average, about 3°F warmer than Hartland. Plymouth, though, has only July and August totally free of ground frost, whereas Hartland is clear of ground frost from May through until October. It must be remembered, however, that the local environment of the

Haytor. The moors — Dartmoor, Exmoor and Bodmin — provide the region with wide variations in its weather. Sunshine on the coast can so easily be replaced by much cooler, cloudier weather by the time the visitor has travelled inland. Haytor on Dartmoor is a favourite spot and the low Cumulus cloud shown here are a common sight. (Meteorological Office)

observation station is an important factor. The Hartland observation point is about 91m (nearly 300ft) above sea-level, whereas the meteorological office at RAF Mount Batten, Plymouth, is 27m (a little less than 90ft) above sea-level. A further example of local variations in temperature was the −17°C (1°F) recorded in the back garden of a weather enthusiast in Newton Abbot one night in February 1979 when the average temperature in South Devon was about −5°C (23°F).

Hawkridge, situated towards the east of Exmoor, has a similar climate to that of Princetown, which is about 91.4m (300ft) higher. Despite the fact that the average temperatures of the two are almost identical, Princetown has the greater extremes of temperature with 30°C (86°F) maximum and −13.3°C (8.1°F) minimum compared with Hawkridge's 25.6°C (78.1°F) and −10.6°C (12.9°F). Despite this, Hawkridge has on average 109 days with ground frost per year against Princetown's 86. In fact there are records of ground frost in Hawkridge during every month of the year. However, it rains in both places on about 220 days a year but Hawkridge has a total of

10

1,526mm (about 60in) while Princetown has 1,924mm (about 76in). So anybody visiting the moors is well advised to take umbrella and raincoat even in the summer, given that it rains on about 19 days in August!

The records clearly show, as one would expect, that on the higher ground rain is more frequent and generally heavier. It is often assumed that places to the west of the moors in the region suffer more rain than those to the east or in the lee of the moors. This is reinforced by statistics with Plymouth, to the west of Dartmoor, having 990mm (about 39in) each year; Exeter to the east having 774mm (about 30in) and Torbay to the south-east having 898mm (about 35in). A further interesting point is that Exeter — some distance inland — has an extreme minimum temperature of −15°C (5°F) against Plymouth and Torbay's −8.9°C (15°F) but all three have the same extreme maximum of about 31°C (88°F). This again shows the influence of the sea on local climatic conditions and it is further emphasised by the 97 days of ground frost at Exeter each year compared with 66 at Plymouth and 50 in Torbay.

The climatic variations in the south-west are well illustrated by the tables at the end of this book which give the climatic conditions for each of the places shown on the map below.

The direction and strength of the wind as well as rain and other forms of precipitation can affect the holiday-maker's destiny quite considerably. Certainly for open-air water sports it is critical: the

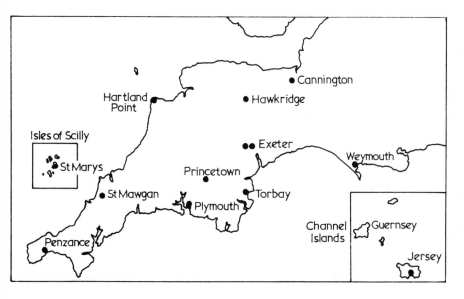

right breeze for a good sail; not too much for the angler in the small boat; the offshore breeze to hold up the wave for the surfer; and, of course, its natural cooling ability on the hotter summer days for those who are less energetic and prefer sunbathing. Even with a windbreak, though, too much wind on the beach can spoil the day. For this reason when choosing a beach it is worth checking the wind direction so that a beach can be chosen that will give the required facility — offshore or onshore as the case may be. Even with quite a strong offshore wind many beaches below high cliffs are apparently wind-free. Unfortunately it is just these conditions which are potentially dangerous to children — or even adults — in small inflatable boats or on air beds. There may be little wind at the water's edge because of the protection of the cliffs, but just a few yards out from shore even a light offshore breeze can suddenly whisk the inflatable out to sea in a very few seconds. The best ploy is never to let children use inflatables with an offshore breeze.

Often in spring and summer on warm sunny days with very little wind, a breeze will develop onshore during the afternoon. This 'sea-breeze' as it is called is caused by the rapid heating of the land which consequently warms the air above it which rises, and cooler air over the sea flows in to take its place; rather like the draught that comes under a door into a warm room. So even if one crosses the peninsula to the opposite coast, the breeze may still be onshore.

Because of the variability of the wind force and direction throughout the year, statistics are rather inconclusive. The Meteorological Office, however, does produce details of wind observations at various places taken at 00, 03, 06, 09, 12, 15, 18, and 21 hours Greenwich Mean Time each day. These show the wind direction in 20° sectors and its force in the Beaufort Scale from 0 to 12, measured as a percentage of total observations.

Data from the following six observation stations in the south-west region have been supplied by the Meteorological Office: St Mary's, Isles of Scilly; St Mawgan; Exeter Airport; Chivenor; Portland Bill and the Lizard. With the exception of Exeter Airport and Chivenor near Barnstaple in North Devon, about one third of all observations show the wind to be force 4 — between 13 and 18 miles per hour. At Exeter and Chivenor, force 3 (8—12 miles per hour) is marginally more prevalent than force 4; together forces 3 and 4 at these stations account for about half the total observations. But at Exeter, interestingly enough, the largest frequency of observations — 27.5% in fact — show the wind to be less than about 5 miles per hour.

Winds of gale force 8 and above (more than about 40 miles per hour) are fortunately not very frequent, but they tend to make news as in the case of the freak storm which hit the Fastnet yacht race competitors in August 1979 and which resulted in the loss of several lives. In nearly all cases these gales tend to be between north-west and south-west at all stations but, occasionally in the winter, a storm from an easterly direction can be most unpleasant. Just such a storm combined with high tides to wreak havoc at the village of Torcross, which faces east across Start Bay, in January 1979.

Because of the variability in wind direction it is difficult to give a definite picture, but at St Mary's, St Mawgan, Chivenor, Portland Bill and the Lizard the wind is within 10° of due west on more occasions than any other direction, while at Exeter Airport this distinction is claimed by west-north-west. Even so, in all cases this only applies to about one observation in eight and so it is also true to say that for nearly ninety per cent of the time the wind is not from these directions!

When winds of gale force and upwards are expected, certain coastguard stations, such as the one on Trevose Head, display a black cone, by day, apex up for a gale expected from a direction north of the east-west line and apex down for a gale expected from a direction south of the east-west line. By night the cone is replaced by a triangle of red or white lights. These signals apply only to the local sea area in which the station is situated and they are, of course, only supplementary to the BBC gale warnings. Nevertheless, they are a useful guide for inshore yachtsmen who have no radio, which hopefully these days is relatively rare.

3 Weather forecasts

The weather being such an important factor in our lives, it is not surprising that there are many people who feel that, in one way or another, they can forecast the weather weeks, months and, in some cases, even years ahead. Their methods are generally unscientific and should not be taken too seriously. The Meteorological Office, even with the vast amount of data, scientific instruments and equipment available to it, plus a world-wide network of observing stations, will usually give a forecast for only a few days ahead. At present the Met. Office is at pains to point out that its monthly 'long-range' statement is not even accorded the name forecast but is generally referred to as 'the prospects for'. This shows that in the present state of the science weather forecasting is not easy. The Met. Office is subjected to criticism, but it is seldom remembered, when a forecast turns out rather wide of the mark, that for well over ninety per cent of the time it is generally correct.

The Meteorological Office at RAF Mount Batten, Plymouth, supplies the information for the weather forecasts given in BBC South West radio and television programmes including the author's forecast in *Spotlight South West*. By telephoning Plymouth 8091 a recorded forecast for Devon and Cornwall can be obtained from the same office. For other areas in the region or for personal advice telephone Plymouth (0752) 42534 or Newquay (06373) 2224 which is the Meteorological Office at RAF St Mawgan.

As a help to understanding the weather forecasts broadcast by the BBC, reproduced overleaf are the television symbols used by the author when presenting the weather forecast in *Spotlight South West*. Also reproduced is the Beaufort wind scale, which gives the definitions in terms of knots and miles per hour of winds force 1—force 12.

Putting it together. The Senior Duty Forecaster at the Plymouth Met. Office at RAF Mount Batten, Les Brown, using a weather map and satellite pictures to give Craig Rich details of the day's forecast.

Television Symbols

(Source: The Meteorological Office)
The new symbols for BBC Television Weather Forecasts are shown below, each with a short explanation. The symbols form a basic language of weather types which can be extended by using various combinations.

 TEMPERATURE: Red figures on a yellow background give positive temperature in degrees centigrade. Black figures on a light blue background give freezing temperatures, ie. below zero centigrade.

 SUNSHINE: The yellow symbol represents the sun; the red figures in the centre show a temperature of 25 degrees centigrade.

 CLOUD: A white cloud symbol indicates fine-weather clouds that may be relatively thin and patchy.

 A black cloud represents the thicker and more widespread clouds often associated with dull weather.

 SUNNY INTERVALS: The sun symbol used in conjunction with a cloud in this way means some sunshine as well, particularly if the white cloud symbol is used.

 RAIN: The dark blue tear-drop symbols beneath the cloud indicate rain.

 RAIN SHOWERS AND SUNNY INTERVALS: A combination of rain, cloud and sun represents sunny intervals and rain showers.

 SNOW: The white snow symbols beneath the cloud indicate snow.

 SLEET: The rain and snow symbols together beneath the cloud indicate sleet.

THUNDERSTORM: The symbol of a black cloud with a yellow flash represents the possibility of thunder and lightning.

 WIND SPEED & DIRECTION: The black symbol represents the wind speed and direction, the speed printed in the centre in white is in miles per hour.

FOG **FOG:** Fog is not represented by a specific symbol; it is indicated by words on the map in the general areas likely to be affected.

Beaufort Scale

Force	Mean speed		Description
	Knots	Miles per hour	
0	0	0	Calm
1	2	2	Light
2	5	5	Light
3	9	10	Light
4	13	15	Moderate
5	19	21	Fresh
6	24	28	Strong
7	30	35	Strong
8	37	42	Gale
9	44	50	Severe Gale
10	52	59	Storm
11	60	68	Violent Storm
12	Above 63	Above 73	Hurricane

Despite the reservations there must be with regard to the amateur weather forecaster, a great deal of weather lore has been handed down over the years and much of this has some relevance — generally the shorter-term it is, the more reliable it is as a predictor. For instance:

> When the rain is from the east,
> it lasts a day or two at least

is quite often true because when Atlantic depressions take the unusual route south-east towards the Mediterranean, southern England comes under the influence of easterly winds and the centre of the depression is then near enough to give long periods of continuous rain. As the speed of the system is quite often slowing up, conditions do not improve until the depression weakens. On the other hand:

> March comes in like a lion,
> and goes out like a lamb

is just not true.

The state and colour of the sky is the basis of much weather lore and, indeed, in the short run much of it has an element of truth. Perhaps the best known and one which has a number of variations is:

> Red sky at night, shepherds' delight,
> Red sky in the morning, shepherds' warning.

This has been said to originate from the Bible, St Matthew, Chapter 16, verses 2 and 3:

> He answered and said unto them, when it is evening,
> ye say, it will be fair weather: for the sky is red,
> And in the morning it will be foul weather today: for
> the sky is red and lowring. O ye hypocrites, ye can
> discern the face of the sky; but can you not discern
> the signs of the times?

Certainly a red sky in the evening is usually a fair weather sign, the glow being caused by the sun's rays striking haze particles in the sky, and a bright red glow under heavy cloud at the beginning of a stormy day often signifies wet weather.

The mackerel, a fish which is currently causing much concern to the fishermen of the south-west, features in several of the sayings concerning the sky. For example:

> Mackerel sky, mackerel sky,
> never long wet and never long dry   and

> Mackerel sky and mares' tails,
> make lofty ships carry low sails.

Both these have a certain amount of truth in them but, nevertheless, it would be unwise to rely on them.

Several other fish are the basis of weather lore such as:

> When trout refuse the bait or fly,
> then ever is a storm a-nigh.

Cirroculumus. A 'mackerel sky' in the south-west has the reputation of bringing bad weather. (R.K. Pilsbury)

Cirrus. Mares' tails — soon these yachts will need to shorten sail. (R.K. Pilsbury)

It is a fact that fish seldom bite when a major change in the weather is impending.

Several animals are also linked to weather lore and cats and dogs are usually good indicators of approaching storms. Dogs sometimes howl while cats get restless.

> Hark! I hear the asses bray;
> we shall have some rain today

is one expression suggesting the forecasting potential of animals and, apparently, asses continue to bray until the weather clears up!

Many people attribute changes in the weather to the moon but apart from controlling the tides it is generally considered to have no effect on the weather. Its help in forecasting, however, springs from the way it lights up cloud formations at night:

> If the moon rises haloed round,
> soon you'll tread on deluged ground

has truth in it because the type of cloud on the advancing edge of a warm front which brings rain, tends to give the moon a halo. These conditions exist about six hours before the rain starts. Cloud formations are also good indicators of the weather. Apart from the references to a mackerel sky we have:

> Hens' scratchings and filly tails,
> make lofty ships carry low sails   and

> If woolly fleeces spread the heavenly way,
> be sure no rain disturbs the summer day.

This latter is a reference to the small white cotton-wool-like clouds characteristic of fine weather.

There is of course much more weather lore which makes interesting and fascinating study but it is worth repeating that it should be used with caution with any but short-term predictions being discounted.

4 A fine summer's day

Today will be warm and sunny with temperatures reaching 20°C (68°F) on coasts and 22°C (72°F) inland. Winds will be light and variable.

The south-west is renowned for its beaches and there is one to cater for every need in most parts of the region. Each has its own particular good and bad points; some are heavily commercialized, but others still remain virtually as nature has developed them. The commercialized beaches have the advantage of providing facilities which parents with young children, in particular, find necessary. On the other hand, the less developed beaches tend not to be so crowded.

A key point to remember is that when weather conditions make one beach unsuitable, only a short drive may take you to another where it is fine. For example, the north coast beaches of Cornwall and Devon stretching either side of Trevose Head, to Woolacombe in the north and St Ives in the south, are a surfer's paradise but quite often a sea mist in the Trevose Head area can ruin a good summer's day on the beach. But only a short drive across the peninsula from Trevose is Carlyon Bay where often the sun is shining brightly when the mist is thick on the north coast. Although the beaches in and around Torbay face eastwards and are sheltered from the prevailing westerly winds, when the wind is onshore they can become uncomfortable, but by driving just a few miles across country to the west of Start Point a beach with a different aspect can be reached.

The ideal conditions for surfing on all suitable beaches are generally a good swell with offshore winds. On the north coasts of Cornwall and Devon, winds between south and east are the best, while winds between north-west and north-east are best for the south-coast beaches. The swell, however, is the main ingredient and this results from strong winds generally associated with depressions in the Atlantic a few days before. The state of the tide is also

21

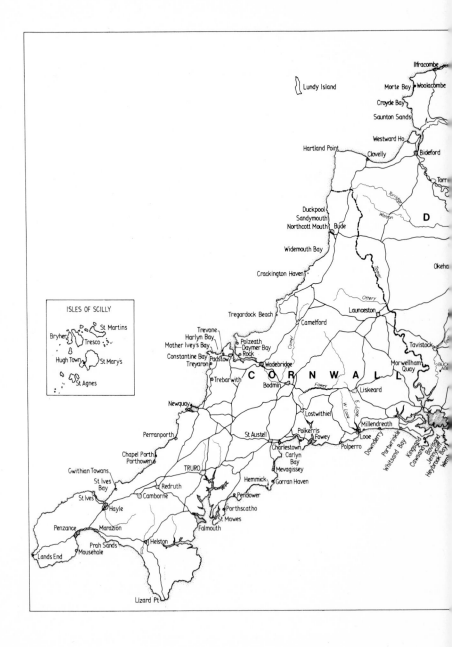

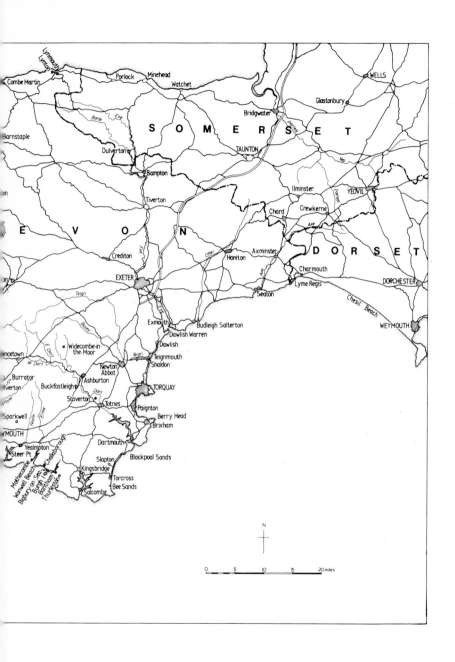

Lynmouth
Lynton
Combe Martin
Porlock
Minehead
Watchet
Barnstaple
S O M E R S E T
WELLS
Glastonbury
Bridgwater
Dulverton
TAUNTON
Bampton
Ilminster
YEOVIL
Tiverton
Chard
Crewkerne
D E V O N
Crediton
Honiton
Axminster
D O R S E T
EXETER
Charmouth
Lyme Regis
DORCHESTER
Teign
Seaton
Exmouth
Budleigh Salterton
Chesil Beach
WEYMOUTH
Dawlish Warren
Widecombe-in-
the-Moor
Dawlish
Princetown
Teignmouth
Shaldon
E Dart
Burrator
Newton
Abbot
Ashburton
TORQUAY
Iverton
Buckfastleigh
Staverton
Paignton
Sparkwell
Totnes
Berry Head
Brixham
PLYMOUTH
Yealmpton
Dartmouth
Steer Pt
Slapton
Blackpool Sands
Mothecombe
Wonwell Beach
Bigbury on Sea
Burgh I
Bantham
Thurlestone
Kingsbridge
Torcross
Bee Sands
Salcombe

Bovey
Erme
W Dart
Plym
Avon
Otter
Exe
Barle
Parrett
Yeo
Axe
Culm

N

0   5   10   15   20 miles

important and the best state varies from beach to beach depending on its topography.

Below are listed some of the beaches which — in the opinion of the author — provide the best facilities for family holiday-makers and perhaps surfing enthusiasts. Many other beaches have been left out because of their inaccessibility. Holiday-makers can watch *Spotlight South West,* the daily early-evening magazine television programme, in which the author gives a detailed weather forecast for the region. In the summer months this is particularly geared to the needs of the holiday-maker.

Beaches and other fair-weather places

Bantham Long, sandy beach, very popular with surfers. Sand dunes. Currents in bay can make swimming extremely dangerous at low water. Car-park in large field (with charge).

Bigbury-on-Sea Highly commercialized, with sandy beaches, bars, restaurants and amusement arcade. Burgh Island, offshore, is worth a visit and can be reached on foot at low water — at other times by tractor.

Blackpool Sands Steep beach, but beautifully clear water, generally making for good swimming.

Bovisand Safe for swimming. Well-known for sub-aqua activities.

Brixham Famous commercial fishing port and popular holiday resort. Angling charter boats can provide superb fishing.

Budleigh Salterton Pebbly beach, seldom crowded. Safe for swimming, apart from where it slopes steeply into the water.

Carlyon Bay Highly commercialized beach: spacious car-park (with charge), restaurant, bar, excellent swimming pool. Boats easily launched from beach, on which there is usually plenty of room. Very clear water, but rather steep in places.

Cawsand Small, pebbly beach. Excellent swimming and sunbathing. Good observation point for the busy activity of Plymouth Sound.

Challaborough Large caravan sites and numerous chalets behind beach. Beach sandy and dangerous for swimming when tide is low.

Chapel Porth Excellent surfing.

Charlestown Old china clay and coal port where small coasters are still manoeuvred in and out by wires operated from the quays. Used in shooting the film *The Eagle Has Landed.*

Blackpool Sands near Dartmouth in South Devon. It offers superb swimming in clear waters. But watch out — especially with children — it has a steeply sloping beach. (Meteorological Office)

Charmouth   Charming village, with massive caravan and chalet parks. Beach a mixture of sand and shingle.

Chesil Beach   The result of millions of pebbles being thrown up by the sea down the centuries. Swimming extremely dangerous at any state of tide. Only the very experienced should launch boats.

Combe Martin   Sandy strip of beach, except at high water. Numerous rock pools to amuse children. Fishing trips, tennis, rowing, riding and putting.

Constantine Bay   Popular beach, excellent for surfing, but inclined to be dangerous, particularly at low water or when tide is ebbing.

Crackington Haven   Surfing beach, generally uncrowded because of its narrow approach lane.

Croyde Bay   Can be dangerous for swimming. Superb surfing in right conditions — a good swell with offshore winds.

Dartmouth   One of the most beautiful towns in the region, on a superb estuary with ceaseless activity. Marina and numerous boat moorings in river. Small maritime museum, castle by the river's mouth and fort. River cruises and angling charters. The Britannia Royal Naval College. Some of *The Onedin Line* filmed here.

Dawlish and Dawlish Warren Attractive resorts with numerous caravan and chalet parks. Golf-course in Dawlish Warren. Amusement arcades and generally safe sandy beaches. Boats for hire.

Daymer Bay Safe swimming.

Downderry Small, generally well-populated beach, with nearby caravan parks and holiday camps.

Duckpool Suitable for surfing, but swimming can be dangerous at certain states of the tide — warning signs and flags should be watched carefully.

Exmouth Popular holiday town, but parts of the long sandy beach can be dangerous for swimming. Watch the signs.

Falmouth Historic port, fallen on hard times commercially, but a thriving holiday resort. Facilities range from fishing trips to summer shows. Best beaches: Gyllyngvase, close to the town and therefore usually busy, with bathing huts, paddling pool and miniature railway; Swanpool, with boating pool. Both generally safe for swimming. Superb municipal gardens. Water skiing areas in many stretches of river.

Fowey Fishing and commercial port, where much of English China Clays Ltd's exports are shipped.

Goodrington One of Torbay's largest and safest beaches.

Gorran Haven Good swimming.

Harlyn Bay Popular surfing beach throughout the year, particularly when wind is south-westerly.

Hayle Dotted with caravan sites and chalets. Swimming on the long, sweeping sandy beach is generally safe except near mouth of River Hayle, at low water or in rough weather.

Hemmick Safe, sheltered swimming, though open to south-westerly winds (not infrequent in the area).

Heybrook Bay Very rocky beaches, popular with skin divers. Close by is the Royal Naval Gunnery School of HMS Cambridge.

Ilfracombe Numerous beaches where swimming is safe on sandy stretches between reefs. Heated indoor swimming pool. Boats can be launched in harbour at high water. Boat trips to Lundy and other places.

Jennycliff Safe swimming, though rocky and pebbly and has to be approached by a cliff path. Close to RAF Mount Batten which houses the Plymouth Meteorological Office.

Kennack Sands Safe swimming in calm weather. Camping and caravan site nearby.

Kingsand Small, pebbly beach. Excellent swimming and

Croyde Bay on the North Devon coast between Barnstaple and Ilfracombe. Like so many beaches along that coastline, it is a fine surfing beach which can offer spectacular sport in the right conditions.

sunbathing. Good view of Plymouth Sound. In summer can be reached by boat service from Plymouth's Sutton Harbour.

Looe Beautiful fishing village with an excellent, if somewhat small, sandy beach with car-park immediately behind. Renowned for fishing trips. Headquarters of the Shark Fishing Club of Great Britain. The Banjo Pier is a favourite shore fishing mark.

Lyme Regis Interesting and historic town with facilities for boating and water-skiing as well as beach amusements, children's playground and aquarium.

Lynmouth and Lynton People come here for the superb cliff scenery and the backcloth of Exmoor but there are several pebbly beaches in this area.

Marazion Famous for proximity to the historical St Michael's Mount. At low water access is by causeway; at high water by ferry. Safe and pleasant bathing west of the causeway on sandy beach.

Mevagissey Old fishing village of great character, protected from the frequent westerly winds in St Austell Bay. Unfortunately only a small beach. A few commercial fishing boats still use harbour, but now more generally associated with angling trips and shark fishing. Popular spot for filming: *Johnny Frenchman* in the late 1940s and, more recently, *Dracula*.

Millendreath Small, generally well-populated beach. Caravan parks and holiday camps nearby.

Minehead Some very fine sandy beaches, large Butlins Holiday Camp, boat trips, cruises, angling charters, summer theatre and a host of amusement arcades and bingo halls. Large rise and fall of tide, so that at low water it is a long trek for a swim.

Morte Bay Good for surfing.

Mothecombe Two beaches, the better of the two being private and open to the public only on Wednesdays and at weekends. Reached by way of Holbeton. Safe swimming on incoming tide.

Mother Ivey's Bay Has large caravan site, and beach for non-caravan owners can only be reached by coastal footpath. Padstow lifeboat housed here.

Mousehole Old fishing village, home of Penlee lifeboat. Beach and swimming and paddling pool.

Newquay Several beaches, numerous hotels, restaurants, ice-cream parlours and even a zoo and a first-class golf-course. Crowded to capacity in peak summer months. Very popular malibu surfing centre. (Part of beach at Watergate Bay is reserved for malibu enthusiasts.) Fistral beach ideal for swimming. (Use of malibu boards is restricted here.)

28

Northcott Mouth   Suitable for surfing, but swimming dangerous at certain states of tide — watch warning signs and flags carefully. Incoming tide should be watched, as it is possible to get cut off.

Padstow   Extremely attractive litle port at mouth of wide Camel estuary. Angling and pleasure trips, including speed-boat rides. Numerous souvenir shops. Small coastal vessels still use port. Home of famous 'Obby Oss'. Passenger ferry connects with Rock.

Paignton   At the centre of the Torbay towns, large safe sandy beach, harbour and many amusement facilities for all weathers.

Pendower   Has sandy area ideal for swimming and safe in most weather conditions.

Penzance   Prosperous and busy town, sheltered from all except south-easterly winds. Swimming-pool on sea front. Sand and shingle beach. Isles of Scilly can be reached from small commercial harbour or heliport.

Perranporth   Ideal for surfing.

Plymouth   By far the largest town in the region. Open-air salt-water swimming pool on foreshore. Small, pebbly beach at Tiniside below the promenade, provides excellent swimming at high water, with rafts moored close off the shore within easy swimming distance. Further small beach at West Hoe, with crazy golf course and small grassy park.

Polkerris   Old fishing village in which many of the cottages have now become holiday homes.

Polperro   Fishing port.

Polzeath   One of the finest surfing beaches on the coast. Ideal for swimming, although the heavy surf can be dangerous for children.

Porthcothan   Popular beach, ideal for surfing, but inclined to be dangerous, particularly at low water or when tide is ebbing.

Porthscatho   Old fishing village, with tiny harbour suitable for sheltering pleasure boats. Ideal spot when westerly winds are in evidence. Sailing and water skiing school.

Porthtowan   Ideal surfing.

Portwrinkle   Small beach, generally well-populated. Caravan sites and holiday camps nearby.

Praa Sands   Particular favourite for surfers, with a two-hundred-yard malibu-board lane reserved at western end of the beach. Large camping and caravan sites surround the sands.

Rock   Can be reached by passenger ferry from Padstow. Thriving dinghy sailing club. Currents can cause danger for unsuspecting swimmers.

St Ives   Very popular holiday resort, open to winds between north-east and north-west. Noted for its artists' colony. Numerous hotels and guest houses. Excellent surfing at Porthmeor beach, but malibu boards restricted to lane marked off at eastern end. Carbis Bay, just out of town, has Atlantic Hotel, caravan and camping site and sandy beach less susceptible to heavy surf than Porthmeor.

St Mawes Important yachting centre.

Salcombe Pretty village, home of the Island Cruising Club and popular yachting and boating centre. Narrow streets and limited parking facilities. Most beaches in the estuary safe for bathing except on the eastern shore immediately opposite ferry landing. All kinds of boats for hire. Angling trips available.

Sandy Mouth Suitable for surfing, but swimming can be dangerous at certain states of the tide. Warning signs and flags should be given close attention.

Saunton Sands Superb surfing in right conditions — generally a good swell and offshore winds. Safe swimming except at north and near rocks.

Seaton Small, often crowded mainly pebble beach, with caravan sites and holiday camps nearby.

Shaldon Opposite Teignmouth at mouth of Teign estuary with famous Ness headland through which there is a tunnel to large secluded sea beach.

Slapton Long, pebbly beach, including Beesands and Torcross. Steep, but beautifully clear water, generally making for good swimming. Particularly suitable for those unable to manage cliff paths.

Steer Point Quiet and peaceful, a popular shore-fishing spot when tide is right and more seaward marks are weather-bound.

Teignmouth About a mile of sandy beach. Safe swimming away from river mouth. Flourishing port where timber is imported and china and ball clay exported. Many hotels and guest houses within a few minutes' walk of station.

Thurlestone Coarse, sandy beach. Safe bathing. Superb golf course.

Torquay The region's largest resort and biggest of the Torbay towns, packed with hotels, guest houses and restaurants. Sandy beaches, crowded especially at high water. Rich night-life, many top performers having summer shows here and at Paignton. Also ideal yachting centre. Numerous parks and other attractions such as Torre Abbey and Cockington.

Trebarwith Strand Suitable for surfing, but completely covered by the sea except at certain states of tide.

Tregardock Beach   As Trebarwith Strand above.

Trevone   Particularly popular when wind is south-westerly.

Treyarnon Bay   Popular beach, ideal for surfing, but inclined to be dangerous particularly at low water or when tide is ebbing.

Wembury   Small beach with numerous rocky pools, close to mouth of River Yealm. Estuary one of most picturesque in South Devon.

Westward Ho!   Long, sandy surf beach, with golf course immediately behind. Many caravan parks and holiday camps.

Weymouth   Very commercialized holiday resort, protected from all except south-east winds. Superb sandy beach. Almost every water activity, including water skiing, but not noted for surf. Car ferries to the Channel Islands and Cherbourg.

Whitesand Bay   Ideal swimming and superb surfing when conditions right. Northern part of the beach is particularly dangerous, like many other beaches on the north Cornwall coast due largely to the strong undertow.

Whitsand Bay   Superb beaches stretching for four miles. Two-hundred-and-fifty-foot cliffs have to be negotiated down one of several well-trodden paths. Only the fit should attempt to descend. Not recommended with a young child 'in arms', or in dubious weather. Superb for swimming, but can be very dangerous, at low water in particular — children should be carefully watched.

Widemouth Bay   Suitable for surfing, but swimming can be dangerous at certain states of the tide — warning signs and flags should be given close attention.

Woolacombe   Two miles of sands, with large car-parks close to the beach. Safe swimming in certain designated areas monitored by life-guards.

Wonwell Beach   Popular barbecue spot, reached via Kingston. Safe for swimming on incoming tide.

Do's and don't's on the beach

(From *Enjoy Sun, Sand and Surf in Safety* published by the Advisory Committee on Beach Life Saving for Devon and Cornwall.)

Do seek and pay attention to the advice of life-guards and others with local knowledge.

Do keep a constant eye on the children and others of the family who cannot swim very well. Small children can drown in quite shallow pools left by the tide.

Do be careful of pot-holes on sandy beaches covered by the sea. Paddlers and pool swimmers can find themselves suddenly out of their depth.

Do read and pay attention to notices, particularly those painted in white lettering on a red ground.

Do pay attention to the Water Safety Code issued by the Royal Society for the Prevention of Accidents (ROSPA).

Do bathe within the area patrolled by life-guards, if possible.

Do look for the position of any life-saving apparatus; and read the instructions on a **Hicks Reel** (if there is one) which will be in a red box, so that you will know how to use it in an emergency.

Do tell the patrol at once if you see any danger.

Do not bathe directly after a meal, or for at least one hour either side of low water.

Do not panic if in difficulty. Lie on your back, keep still, raise one arm and shout.

Do not allow your family to use air-beds or inflatable rings or toy animals to support themselves in the water, except under strict supervision. They can be carried away by wind or current, and are **very dangerous.**

Do not exhaust yourself by swimming against the tide or a current. Float, raise one arm and shout.

Do not leave litter on the beach. Not only is it unsightly but broken glass, opened tins and so on are **very dangerous** to humans and animals alike.

Do not enter the water when the red flag is flying (A number of people were fined by a magistrates' court for so doing in Cornwall in 1979.)

Fair-weather cumulus. Typical cloud on a fine summer's day in the south—west. (R.K. Pilsbury)

Emergency

If you require assistance to deal with an incident in the sea or on the cliff face, dial 999 on the telephone.

When the operator asks what service you require, ask for Coastguard.

When the coastguard answers, tell him—

1. where you are,
2. nature and exact position of the incident.
3. the telephone number you are phoning from and at which you can be contacted.

If possible, arrange for someone who is in the picture, to remain at the telephone, in case the coastguard requires further information.

Signals

The danger flag   On all popular beaches a life-guard or other person charged with the duty is responsible for hoisting the red danger flag when he considers the conditions are such as to warrant it. He has to make up his mind, and then stick to his decision. He will lower the flag as soon as he is satisfied that conditions have again become safe, so do not dispute his action. To leave the flag flying when it is no longer necessary causes doubt in the minds of the public and tends to bring the use of the danger warning into disrepute.

The flag will be lowered when the responsible person goes off duty in the evening even though it may still be unsafe to bathe. This again is because of the importance of maintaining the authority of the warning. It may become a dead flat calm later in the evening or by early morning, giving people the idea that the hoisted flag can be ignored.

The public is warned that the absence of the danger flag when the life-guard is *not* on duty does not necessarily mean that it is safe to bathe, and you should do so with caution.

Red and yellow flags The use of small red and yellow flags to denote patrolled bathing areas is at the discretion of the local authority concerned. If a life-guard is authorised to use them he will actually, and so far as possible continuously, patrol the area that he has marked out. The public is strongly advised to bathe only between these flags.

Cliff climbing

Many accidents occur every year in the west country when people attempt to climb cliffs. These accidents are often fatal. **You are advised not to climb cliffs at all.**

Underwater swimming

The British Sub-Aqua Club advises that underwater swimming with mask, fins and snorkel tube can be dangerous if a few simple rules are not observed, and the Club is concerned about the number of children and young people taking to 'snorkel diving' without sufficient tuition. You should be very careful in allowing your family to 'snorkel'.

(Further information on surf life-saving can be obtained from the National Secretary, The Surf Life Saving Association of Great Britain, 4 Cathedral Yard, Exeter EX1 1HJ.)

5   A poor day

Today will be cloudy with occasional rain or drizzle. Temperatures will be a little below normal for the time of year.

The majority of people who come to the south-west for a summer holiday do so because they hope to bask on the beach in the sun. Due to the vagaries of our weather there are days, even in high summer, when this is not possible and an alternative must be found.

Shopping for presents to take back home tends to be left until the last minute. It makes sense, therefore, to head, on the first poor day, for a reasonably sized town, where there is not only a wider choice of shops but, in many cases, other attractions which may compensate for not being able to go on the beach. On the other hand, it should be remembered that towns tend to get very crowded when the weather is bad in summer, with many holiday-makers heading haphazardly for the nearest built-up area.

Below are lists of towns and other places of interest suitable for poor weather. As well as these, many of the Royal National Lifeboat Institution's boat-houses are open to the public and are well worth a visit. (St Ives is an example.) On a maritime theme, lighthouses, such as the Trevose Head Lighthouse, are also open to the public.

Poor-weather places

Bampton   Famous for October fair, when Exmoor ponies which have been rounded up are sold.

Barnstaple   All roads lead to the Friday market in the centre of this picturesque town, dominated by Georgian architecture. Leisure centre.

Bideford   Attractive town, still operating as port. Coasters discharge timber at quays. Downstream at Appledore a thriving shipbuilding yard. Zoo on outskirts of town. Georgian architecture. Barnstaple and Bideford the most important towns in North Devon.

Bodmin Fifteenth-century parish church, the largest in Cornwall. Old county jail, now housing night-club. Fine public indoor swimming pool. Bodmin Farm Park, at Fletcher's Bridge, open to public.

Buckfastleigh Famous for wine and honey produced by monks of Buckfast Abbey, built by Benedictines in first third of this century. Northern terminal of Dart Valley Railway, owned by steam engine enthusiasts. The half-hour journey to Totnes takes in beautiful countryside.

Buckland Abbey Once the home of Drake and now open to public, including Drake Naval and West Country Folk Museum.

Burrator This reservoir supplies most of the Plymouth area with water. Picturesque spot surrounded by pine trees — very popular afternoon drive for residents of the area, even in winter.

Camborne and Redruth Boiler-house of Cornish Rugby and at one time heart of the world's most productive copper-mining area and a major source of tin. Camborne famous for its School of Mines and also has Holman Museum.

Chard Notable for superb wildlife park at nearby Cricket St Thomas which has 1,000 acres of beautiful parkland, part of which is stocked with large collection of wild animals and birds.

Clovelly A must. One of the quaintest and prettiest villages in the region. Old colour-washed cottages, built on side of the cliff. Cobbled main street descends in steps to stone harbour. All supplies delivered by donkey, although landrovers can reach harbour by a back track. Lifeboat in harbour with impressive record of lives saved. Substantial car-park above village.

Crediton Said to be birthplace of St Boniface. Now a market town with fine, large, red sandstone church.

Dartington Medieval estate and house, now centre for adult education with emphasis on arts. Dartington glass originated here.

Dulverton Ancient market town, now a centre for shooting, riding and fishing. (River Barle runs through town.)

Exeter County town of Devon. Considerably smaller than Plymouth, but with its own unique qualities. Cathedral. Guildhall claimed to be oldest municipal building in country (on present site since 1160). Maritime Museum, with a number of boats afloat in Exeter ship canal basin and, indoors, biggest collection of its kind in the world.

Honiton Centre for antique trades. Known for lace, still produced on modest scale.

Land's End Highly commercialized. Large car-park, souvenir

Altocumulus. Just ahead of a cold front — a sign of instability in the air and that thunderstorms may be brewing. (R.K. Pilsbury)

shops, snack bars and an hotel. Superb view out to sea over Longships Lighthouse — photographers abound.

Launceston Once the ancient county town of Cornwall. Georgian houses surround central shopping square. Remains of Norman castle. Jamaica Inn (on which Daphne Du Maurier based her famous novel) is not far out of town; Dozmary Pool also nearby and worth a visit.

Lizard Point Cornwall's most southerly tip, rich vegetation showing the climate in the far west really is milder.

Lundy Island Measures about 3 miles by just under a mile, windswept. Only about 20 inhabitants. Buildings: thirteenth-century castle; hotel; pub (open when ships arrive); church; some cottages. Reached, between March and October, by passenger service from Ilfracombe. (One-way trip takes about 1½ hours.) In winter the vessel *Polar Bear* operates as supply ship on Tuesdays and Fridays.

Lynmouth and Lynton Lynton is some 150m (500ft) above pretty harbour of Lynmouth. Water-operated cliff railway runs between the two. Exmoor Museum.

One of the most exciting and talked about pleasures in the south-west — shark fishing. During the season, dozens of boats leave places like Looe, Polperro, Mevagissey, Plymouth or the River Torridge in search of one of the kings of the sea. In a good season hundreds will be hooked and brought shore in Devon and Cornwall. (West Country Tourist Board)

Morwellham Quay   Once a thriving port on the Tamar. Can be visited by boat trip from Plymouth, or by road from Tavistock/Gunnislake.

Newton Abbot   Visit the Wednesday market.

Okehampton   Market town and tourist centre for exploring Dartmoor. Within walking distance of High Willhays and Yes Tor, (both over 600m, 2,000ft, above sea-level). Nearby, the Pine Valley Wild Life Park.

Paignton Zoo   Large collection of animals and birds from all over world. Open every day of year.

Penzance   Museum of Nautical Art. Beautiful municipal gardens.

Plymouth   By far the largest city in the region. The Barbican: the Mayflower Steps, from which Pilgrim Fathers set sail for America; Sutton Pool, now being developed as yachting marina, with many old warehouses becoming expensive appartments; commercial fishing vessels still using port; thriving fish market held every morning except Sunday; deep-sea angling charter boats, to the Eddystone Reef and deep-water wrecks further out. Near the Barbican, many antique and souvenir shops, fashionable restaurants and pubs with historic connections. The world-famous Hoe: Royal Navy War Memorial; statue of Sir Francis Drake; Smeaton's Tower (lighthouse originally situated on the Eddystone rocks); Marine Biological Association's aquarium. Millbay Docks, one of the commercial areas of the port. Municipal heated indoor swimming pool in Central Park. Mayflower sports centre, with, nearby, outdoor putting greens and miniature golf course. Devonport Dockyard (open to public during August Bank Holiday weekend).

Porlock   Narrow winding streets and quaint harbour. Thirteenth-century parish church.

Princetown   On Dartmoor, the highest inhabited town in England, some 430m (1,400ft) above sea-level. Dartmoor Prison.

Redruth   As under Camborne.

Scilly, Isles of   Fascinating group of islands with such temperate climate that spring flowers bloom before Christmas. St Mary's (on which, amongst others, the Prince of Wales and Sir Harold Wilson have properties) is reached by helicopter or ship from Penzance.

Sparkwell   Dartmoor Wildlife Park — mainly wildlife common to Europe.

Tavistock   Largely famous as parish of Sir Francis Drake's birth and for 'Goosie' fair held in October.

Tiverton   Has remains of fourteenth-century castle. Blundells, famous public school founded nearly four hundred years ago. Horse boat trips on Grand Western Canal.

Torrington   Pretty market town, perched high above River Torridge. Superb view from car-park on edge of town. Dartington glass factory.

Torquay   The spectacular Kents Cavern is worth seeing; also model village.

Totnes   Popular tourist spot. River trips through some of the most beautiful scenery in Devon. Rich in bookshops.

Truro   The only city in Cornwall, administrative centre and capital in all but name. Cathedral. Museum. Substantial car-park near River Truro. Boat trips down river.

Widecombe-in-the-Moor   Picturesque village, known for its fair and the problems of Old Uncle Tom Cobley. Fourteenth-century church. The Church House, a National Trust property, and Glebe House.

Yealmpton   Devon Shire Horse farm — fascinates children. Kitley Caves nearby.

Historic Sutton Pool in Plymouth's Barbican area. The old warehouses that used to be a main part of Plymouth's sea trading days are being converted into apartments, wine bars and restaurants. The Barbican and its fish market are a great attraction for visitors throughout the year.

Large cumulus. Possibility of a shower? Unstable atmospheric conditions. (R.K. Pilsbury)

Leisure centres

The full list of leisure centres in the region as supplied by the Westcountry Tourist Board is as follows:

Devon
Kitto Sports Centre
Honicknowle Lane,
Plymouth.
Tel. Plymouth (0752) 702492
Facilities: Main hall, 1 squash court.

Mayflower Sports Centre
Central Park,
Plymouth.
Tel. Plymouth (0752) 54112
Facilities: Main hall, bowling hall, five-a-side hall.

North Devon Sports and Leisure Centre
Seven Brethren Bank,
Barnstaple.
Tel. Barnstaple (0271) 73361

41

Facilities: Main hall, indoor swimming pool, learner pool, diving pit, 4 squash courts, bowling hall.

Cornwall
Carn Brea Leisure Centre
Pool,
Nr. Redruth.
Tel. Camborne (0209) 4766
Facilities: Main hall, indoor swimming pool, learner pool, diving pit, 4 squash courts, projectile room, outdoor athletics track.

Polkyth Recreational Centre
St Austell.
Tel. St Austell (0726) 4466
Facilities: Main hall, indoor swimming pool, learner pool, diving pit, 4 squash courts.

Somerset
Wellington Sports Centre
Corams Lane,
Wellington.
Tel. Wellington (082 347) 3010
Facilities: Main hall, indoor swimming pool, 4 squash courts, projectile range, outdoor tennis courts.

The National Trust

Below is a list of some of the National Trust properties in the region.

Cornwall
Antony House, Torpoint, near Plymouth Eighteenth-century house with central block of Pentewan stone.
Cornish Engines, Pool near Camborne Two Cornish beam mine engines, examples of one of the earliest applications of steam power to industry.
Cotehele, near Plymouth Medieval house of grey granite built around two courts on foundations of earlier house.
Lanhydrock, near Bodmin Seventeenth-century house largely rebuilt after a fire in 1881.
Lawrence House, Launceston Local museum.
St Michael's Mount, Marazion Castle on Benedictine chapel site.

Tintagel Old Post Office Fourteenth-century stone house built to plan of medieval manor house.

Trerice, near Newquay Manor house rebuilt in 1571.

Devon

Arlington Court, near Barnstaple House, built 1822, contains small objets d'art, model ships, shells, pewter, costume and furniture.

Bradley Manor, Newton Abbot Small, rough-cast fifteenth-century manor house with great hall.

Buckland Abbey, near Plymouth Thirteenth-century monastery bought by Sir Francis Drake in 1581.

Castle Drogo at Drewsteignton, near Chagford Granite castle built between 1910 and 1930 by Sir Edward Lutyens. Stands over 900 ft overlooking wooded gorge of the River Teign.

Compton Castle, near Torquay A fortified manor house built in three stages (1320, 1440 and 1520). Restored after 1930.

Knightshayes Court, near Tiverton Begun in 1870 the house stands in a large area of woodland on the east side of the Exe Valley overlooking Tiverton.

Loughwood Meeting House, near Axminster Built 1653 by Baptist congregation of Kilmington.

Saltram, near Plymouth Originally a Tudor house with classical facades added in the eighteenth century.

Sharpitor, Salcombe Overbeck Museum: collection of butterflies and shells with section devoted to shipbuilding. Especially good for children.

Shute Barton, near Axminster Remains of manor house built over three centuries and completed in late sixteenth century.

Watersmeet Cottage, near Lynmouth Fishing lodge completed in 1832.

Somerset

Barrington Court, near Ilminster Sixteenth-century house with Gothic and Renaissance features.

Coleridge Cottage, near Bridgwater Coleridge's home for three years and where he wrote *The Ancient Mariner*.

Dunster Castle, near Minehead Castle dating from thirteenth century. Remodelled by Anthony Salvin in the nineteenth century.

Dorset

Hardy's Cottage, Higher Brockhampton, near Dorchester Small thatched cottage where novelist and poet Thomas Hardy was born.

6 Weather disasters

In the earlier chapters of this book a number of freak weather phenomena have been mentioned in passing and may have aroused the reader's interest. For this reason, the final chapter of this book is devoted to a more detailed look at some of the unexpected extreme conditions which have affected the south-west region during the past thirty years. It should be emphasised, though, that it is the unexpected and the unusual that are remembered. Generally speaking, the weather pattern in those thirty years has deviated very little from the normal.

Lynmouth 1952

During the night of 15—16 August about two hundred and fifty miles of North Devon and West Somerset were severely flooded. At Lynmouth about thirty people lost their lives when the River Lyn — swollen by 229mm (9in) of rain which fell between 11.30am on 15 August and 9am on the 16 August — burst its banks and changed its course during the night, sending a wall of water, described by residents as resembling a huge tidal wave, down the main street.

The torrent carried with it an avalanche of huge boulders and uprooted numerous tree trunks. All the bridges over the West Lyn were destroyed and houses, hotels and shops inundated or wrecked. Motor vehicles were swept out to sea and the electricity, gas, water and sewerage systems rendered useless. The majority of the sea wall was demolished and the road from Lynmouth to Lynton destroyed. Holiday-makers marooned on the roofs of hotels were rescued by army amphibious vehicles and rushed to area rest centres at Lynton, Minehead and Barnstaple.

A number of people were drowned at Barbrook near Lynmouth and near South Molton three boy scouts were drowned when floods swept away their camp. A man lost his life in the West Somerset village of Parracombe. Although there was no loss of life in

44

Dulverton, many houses were demolished there, and in Exford, as a result of the flooding of the Rivers Exe and Barle.

A detailed inspection on 18 August by Mr Harold MacMillan, Minister of Housing and Local Government, revealed that damage to roads and bridges in Devon was estimated at £350,000 and to the public services as a whole at £2,000,000. In Lynmouth, 42 houses were destroyed and in Devon a total of 17 bridges collapsed.

The conditions which led up to the disaster began with a warm spell in the second half of July and an absolute drought over a large part of southern England. These conditions broke down at the beginning of August and were replaced by a period of changeable weather over the whole country. It rained frequently, often heavily, and there were thunderstorms somewhere in the country every day. The rainfall on Exmoor was particularly heavy and so immediately before the Lynmouth flood the ground was unusually wet for the time of year especially in the large boggy area on Exmoor which is the source of the West Lyn river.

Continuous rain began in the far west of Cornwall early on the 15 August and spread to all parts of Cornwall, Devon and Somerset by midday. The nearest weather recording station to Lynmouth showed eighteen hours or more of non-stop rain. Longstone Barrow, at the headwaters of streams which drain down to Lynmouth, had 152mm (6in) between 7pm and midnight on 15 August; 178mm (7in) between 5pm and midnight. Such a heavy fall of rain would apparently be enough to cause flooding in any normally situated position. At Lynmouth the situation was aggravated by the topography of the northern edge of Exmoor, which lies immediately behind it, and where a wide stretch of land falls from a height of 457.2m (1,500ft) to the sea in a distance of about four miles. The total rainfall amounted to more than 500,000 tons of water per square mile and this came pouring down the hillside in the raging torrent that engulfed the town.

East Devon 1968

The worst floods in living memory occurred in East Devon on 11 July 1968 when 63.5mm (2.5in) of rain fell in the course of an hour. Thousands of pounds worth of damage was caused and road and rail communications were severely disrupted. An elderly lady was drowned in her riverside cottage at Sidmouth and about 30 people had to be rescued from the floodwaters. The main roads — pre-M5 days — were badly flooded and one of the Fenny Bridges on the

A30 between Exeter and Honiton was carried away. Altogether six bridges were washed away, including one, which was replaced by a Bailey bridge, near Marsh on the Devon—Somerset border.

The floods also severely damaged cereal crops in the Taw and Torridge valleys in North Devon and panic newspaper reports warned holiday-makers to avoid the area although, locally, this advice was challenged by the authorities who had the situation under control almost immediately.

The summer drought 1976

The long hot summer of 1976 resulted in 10,000 stand-pipes being erected in order to ration water in the North Devon and Plymouth areas. The Drought Act, hastily rushed through Parliament, made it illegal to wash cars, to fill swimming pools, to water golf courses and sports grounds or to clean the exterior of buildings. Many acres of arable land were reduced to a dusty waste and crops and grass died in the unrelenting scorch of the sunshine.

By mid-August, with the last measurable fall of rain, 6.35mm (0.25in), more than a month before, the amount of water in the River Tamar was down to 7 per cent of its average monthly flow; the River Exe to 8 per cent; and the River Taw to 6 per cent. At Fernworthy reservoir the drought resulted in an old road bridge surfacing; it had not been seen since the first flooding of the reservoir in the 1940s.

As an example of the dangers caused by the drought, 150 heath and grassland fires had to be dealt with by firemen in Devon and Cornwall on the 18 August. And the extreme heat which caused Plymouth's hottest June day, measured at 28°C (83°F), since records began in 1921 and which made inland temperatures soar into the 30s Centigrade (90s Fahrenheit) resulted in a 67 year old man dying while swimming at Teignmouth and a 56 year old woman collapsing and dying at Challaborough. Medical Officers warned that sudden immersion in cold sea water after lying in the abnormally hot sun could be fatal.

Stand-pipes were used in some places, notably at Tavistock and Okehampton, much to the chagrin of the residents. Fortunately the weather broke during the August Bank Holiday weekend when the first substantial fall of rain for many weeks was experienced in the south-west of England.

Polperro 1976

On Friday night of 24-25 September 1976, with the drought only four weeks behind and stand-pipes still being used to ration water in Okehampton, continuous heavy rain brought disaster to the pretty fishing village of Polperro. The narrow streets, so often packed with holiday-makers, were turned into raging waterways as the heavy rain building up in the hills around the village suddenly surged downwards in a wall of water 1½m (5ft) high, which smashed into the streets sweeping debris before it and causing one man to lose his life, the power to fail (putting the village in darkness) and cars to be tossed about like flotsam, smashing into walls or being unceremoniously dumped into the raging torrent which a few hours earlier had been a quiet trickling stream.

Many houses were inundated and when the flood subsided a carpet of mud lay everywhere and debris was piled up in the streets. It took several weeks for the village to get back to normal and a disaster fund was set up in an effort to attract support from some of the millions of visitors who had found the village so picturesque.

The blizzards 1978

In mid-February 1978 most of Devon, Dorset, Somerset and part of Cornwall was one big snowdrift. Some homes were cut off for days, scores of farm animals were lost in twenty-foot snowdrifts, roads were blocked and life was virtually brought to a standstill.

RAF helicopters worked around the clock to help people in North Devon and on 19 February rescued 120 people from the Arctic-like wastes — more than in the whole of the previous year. The helicopters were also needed to aid kidney patients whose dialysis machines were inoperative due to power cuts. Expectant mothers, nearing confinement, were helicoptered to hospital from outlying areas and groups of lorry drivers and motorists were airlifted to safety from their stranded vehicles on the Bampton—South Molton road. At Broadhembury near Honiton the bride, groom and thirty guests at a wedding reception were marooned for four days.

Helicopters from RNAS Culdrose flew sorties from Exerter Airport on a number of days dropping fodder to animals, and food to outlying farms, which were cut off for weeks. Telephone and power lines were severed in many places, making communication impossible. The main Exeter—Plymouth and Exeter—Torbay roads were impassable for more than a day at Haldon Hill and Telegraph

47

Torcross. The coasts around the south-west lie exposed to the full force of the weather. The gales that lashed Torcross in Devon almost destroyed a community. Rebuilding and new sea defences should make sure that the village will not be battered again. (BBC South West)

Hill and on the 19 February the residents of Exeter awoke to find the thickest blanket of snow in living memory covering the city. Twenty-foot snowdrifts surrounded the hamlet of Sheepstor for more than three days and a major operation was mounted to dig out sheep buried beneath the snowdrifts. At the South West Water Authority's hatcheries at South Molton on the edge of Exmoor, 30,000-40,000 rainbow trout perished when the leats supplying water to the fish were completely blocked by falling snow and the build-up of ice.

As is so often the case with heavy snowfalls, if a rapid thaw sets in, flooding occurs. This happened after the blizzards and on 22 February flood water was seven feet deep in Kingsbridge. Residents were evacuated from their homes to higher ground when, ironically, some people were still cut off in the snowdrifts to the north. In fact the Tavistock—Okehampton road was blocked for a week.

The Fastnet Race in 1979. One of the worst yachting disasters ever came as a ferocious storm hit the fleet of boats between Ireland and the south-west of England. The skill and courage of the armed forces and lifeboatmen saved dozens of people. But several were lost. (BBC South West)

Torcross 1979

On the night of 3 January 1979, the neighbouring villages of Torcross and Beesands, just north of Start Point, were left devastated by the worst storms experienced there for more than sixty years. In January 1918, the nearby hamlet of Hallsands was completely destroyed by a similar storm with ferocious winds from the south—east. Running north—south the coastline is particularly vulnerable to strong easterlies and on the night in question winds gusting up to 70 miles per hour combined with high tides and low barometric pressure to send huge waves crashing into the two villages. At Torcross, two buildings were washed away, the foundations of many others undermined and many houses had their roofs ripped off.

Other east-facing coastal towns in the region suffered harm, notably Penzance where the sea defences were damaged and many fishing boats sunk at their moorings. Teignmouth and Weymouth were flooded while snow which had been cleared only a few days previously was blown back onto moorland roads by the ferocity of the winds. In Jersey the storm, combined with the worst blizzard for many years, caused the island's schools to be closed.

The Fastnet Yacht Race 1979

On the night of Monday 13 August 1979, more than 300 yachts were stretched out between Cowes and Fastnet on the outward-bound stretch of the race. An Atlantic depression to the west of Ireland, which was expected to bring gales to the sea areas around the west country, was deepening ominously — far more than is usual for depressions at that time of the year. As it approached the stretch of sea between Land's End and southern Ireland it turned into one of the worst storms to hit the area in high summer for many years, with winds of up to force 10 (a mean speed of about 60 miles per hour) together with torrential rain.

The seas became so furious that many yachts were lost or abandoned and fifteen yachtsmen lost their lives to make it the worst yachting disaster of all time. Only the dedicated work of the Royal National Lifeboat Institution crews, the Coastguard, Royal Navy helicopter crews and ships, including the Dutch destroyer *Overiissel* acting as guard-ship for the race fleet, prevented the race being an even bigger disaster.

On land many trees were uprooted, holiday-makers found their tents blown away and several caravans were damaged. Damage was also caused to houses, many loosing slates and tiles from their roofs.

The above examples of extreme weather conditions in the region are particularly interesting in that, apart from the 1978 blizzards and Torcross, they occurred during the summer-holiday months. It is however worth re-emphasising that, taken over a period of time, the overall weather pattern of the region remains much the same; the unusual and unexpected will always make the headlines and be remembered.

Appendix: Climatological tables

(Source: The Meteorological Office)

Cannington   Height: 23m (75.5ft)

	Average temperatures				*Average rainfall*		*Average sunshine*	*Average number of days frost*	
	Centigrade		*Fahrenheit*						
					Per month		*Days per month*	*Hours per day*	*Air*	*Ground*
	Max.	*Min.*	*Max.*	*Min.*	*mm*	*in*				
Jan.	7.4	1.8	45.3	35.2	70	2.8	16	1.70	9.0	14.4
Feb.	7.6	1.8	45.7	35.2	49	1.9	13	2.68	9.6	14.8
Mar.	10.3	2.9	50.5	37.2	45	1.8	14	4.03	5.5	12.2
April	13.3	5.1	55.9	41.2	49	1.9	15	5.71	1.4	7.7
May	16.2	7.4	61.2	45.3	63	2.5	16	6.63	0.1	1.9
June	19.0	10.9	66.2	51.6	44	1.7	14	7.20	—	0.3
July	20.7	12.6	69.3	54.7	60	2.4	11	6.66	—	—
Aug.	20.3	12.5	68.5	54.5	73	2.9	13	5.93	—	—
Sept.	18.4	10.7	65.1	51.3	63	2.5	13	4.53	—	0.3
Oct.	15.1	8.0	59.2	46.4	67	2.6	14	3.24	—	2.5
Nov.	10.7	4.8	51.3	40.6	82	3.2	17	2.10	2.9	9.7
Dec.	8.5	3.0	47.3	47.4	72	2.8	16	1.68	7.4	13.4
Extremes	33.3	−15.6	91.9	3.9	—	—	—	—	—	—
Year	14.0	6.8	57.2	44.2	737	29.0	172	1587.7	35.9	77.2

Exeter Airport   Height: 32m (105ft)

	Average temperatures				Average rainfall		Average sunshine	Average number of days frost	
	Centigrade		Fahrenheit						
					Per month		Days per month	Hours per day	Air	Ground
	Max.	Min.	Max.	Min.	mm	in				
Jan.	7.4	2.4	45.3	36.3	83	3.3	17	1.74	9.6	15.5
Feb.	7.7	2.1	45.9	35.8	58	2.3	14	2.68	9.2	15.4
Mar.	10.3	3.1	50.5	37.6	55	2.2	15	3.97	5.6	15.6
April	13.2	4.8	55.8	40.6	47	1.9	15	5.64	2.2	10.9
May	16.0	7.1	60.8	44.8	61	2.4	14	6.52	0.5	5.1
June	19.2	10.1	66.6	50.2	41	1.6	12	6.90	—	1.2
July	20.6	11.9	69.1	53.4	51	2.0	10	6.16	—	0.1
Aug.	20.4	11.6	68.7	52.9	68	2.7	12	5.69	—	0.3
Sept.	18.4	10.2	65.1	50.4	67	2.6	11	4.48	—	1.3
Oct.	15.0	7.8	59.0	46.0	72	2.8	14	3.25	0.4	5.2
Nov.	10.7	4.9	51.3	40.8	90	3.5	18	2.17	5.5	12.4
Dec.	8.4	3.3	47.1	37.9	81	3.2	18	1.78	8.4	14.4
Extremes	30.6	−15.0	87.1	5.0	—	—	—	—	—	—
Year	13.9	6.6	57.0	43.9	774	30.5	170	1553.8	41.4	97.4

Hartland Point
Height: 91m (298.6ft)

	Average temperatures				Average rainfall			Average sunshine	Average number of days frost	
	Centigrade		Fahrenheit							
					Per month		Days	Hours		
	Max.	Min.	Max.	Min.	mm	in	per month	per day	Air	Ground
Jan.	7.3	4.3	33.8	39.4	81	3.2	18	1.78	4.6	6.8
Feb.	6.9	3.5	44.4	38.3	56	2.2	13	2.72	4.5	7.1
Mar.	8.8	4.7	47.8	40.5	57	2.2	14	4.34	1.6	4.9
April	10.7	6.4	51.3	43.5	51	2.0	16	6.16	0.3	1.1
May	13.2	8.6	55.8	47.5	58	2.3	15	7.12	—	—
June	15.8	11.4	60.4	52.5	53	2.1	12	7.36	—	—
July	17.3	13.2	63.1	55.8	71	2.8	13	6.39	—	—
Aug.	17.5	13.5	63.5	56.3	83	3.3	16	6.10	—	—
Sept.	16.3	12.4	61.3	54.3	79	3.1	15	4.83	—	—
Oct.	13.9	10.1	57.0	50.2	86	3.4	17	3.43	—	—
Nov.	10.4	7.1	50.7	44.8	97	3.8	19	2.02	0.1	0.8
Dec.	8.5	5.5	47.3	41.9	94	3.7	18	1.56	3.7	6.4
Extremes	31.1	−8.9	88.0	16	—	—	—	—	—	—
Year	12.2	8.4	54.0	47.1	866	34.1	186	1640.3	14.8	27.1

Hawkridge (Exmoor)   Height: 314m (1,030ft)

| | Average temperatures | | | | Average rainfall | | Average sunshine | Average number of days frost | |
| | Centigrade | | Fahrenheit | | Per month | | Days per month | Hours per day | Air | Ground |
	Max.	Min.	Max.	Min.	mm	in				
Jan.	5.5	0.7	41.9	33.3	160	6.3	22	1.10	13.0	18.1
Feb.	5.3	0.3	41.5	32.5	121	4.8	16	2.03	14.1	19.1
Mar.	7.7	1.5	45.9	34.7	99	3.9	18	3.77	10.2	18.9
April	10.5	3.5	50.9	38.3	95	3.7	20	4.82	2.8	10.7
May	13.5	5.8	56.3	42.4	103	4.1	17	5.64	0.4	3.1
June	16.5	8.8	61.7	47.8	79	3.1	14	6.36	—	0.7
July	17.6	10.2	63.7	50.4	105	4.1	16	5.97	—	0.1
Aug.	17.3	10.5	63.1	50.9	134	5.3	19	5.49	—	0.1
Sept.	15.5	9.1	59.9	48.4	135	5.3	18	4.38	—	1.1
Oct.	12.5	6.8	54.5	44.2	140	5.5	22	2.88	0.1	3.4
Nov.	8.5	3.6	47.3	38.5	171	6.7	23	2.26	4.6	13.4
Dec.	6.6	1.7	43.9	35.1	184	7.2	21	1.34	11.8	19.9
Extremes	25.6	−10.6	78.1	12.9	—	—	—	—	—	—
Year	11.4	5.2	52.5	41.4	1526	60.0	226	1403.2	57.0	108.6

Jersey (St Louis Observatory)   Height: 47m (154.2ft)

	Average temperatures				Average rainfall		Average sunshine		Average number of days frost	
	Centigrade		Fahrenheit							
					Per month		Days per month	Hours per day	Air	Ground
	Max.	Min.	Max.	Min.	mm	in				
Jan.	7.9	3.7	46.2	38.7	94	3.7	20	2.15		13
Feb.	8.1	3.6	46.6	38.5	66	2.6	15	3.10		13
Mar.	10.6	4.9	49.1	40.8	54	2.1	13	5.07		10
April	13.1	6.8	55.6	44.2	52	2.1	13	7.01		5
May	16.2	9.2	61.2	48.6	53	2.1	12	7.92		1
June	18.9	11.8	66.0	53.2	40	1.6	10	8.35		0
July	20.7	13.5	69.3	56.3	48	1.9	11	8.13	No	0
Aug.	20.6	13.9	69.1	57.0	71	2.8	14	7.25	Record	0
Sept.	19.0	12.9	66.2	55.2	72	2.8	15	5.61		0
Oct.	15.8	10.6	60.4	51.1	80	3.2	15	4.13		1
Nov.	11.7	7.3	53.1	45.1	111	4.4	19	2.41		5
Dec.	9.3	5.1	48.7	41.2	111	4.4	20	1.84		10
Extremes	35	−10	95	14	—	—	—	—		—
Year	14.3	8.6	57.7	47.5	852	33.7	177	1922.1		58

Penzance

Height: 19m (62.3ft)

	Average temperatures				Average rainfall		Average sunshine	Average number of days frost	
	Centigrade		Fahrenheit						
					Per month		Days per month	Hours per day	Air	Ground
	Max.	Min.	Max.	Min.	mm	in				
Jan.	9.4	4.5	48.9	40.1	127	5.0	20	1.95	4.2	10.2
Feb.	9.2	3.9	48.6	39.0	90	3.5	18	2.93	4.2	10.9
Mar.	10.8	5.3	51.4	41.5	85	3.4	17	4.17	2.2	12.5
April	13.0	6.6	55.4	43.9	61	2.4	16	6.34	0.4	5.9
May	15.3	8.8	59.5	47.8	75	3.0	17	7.18	—	1.2
June	18.1	11.2	64.6	52.2	56	2.2	14	7.30	—	—
July	19.5	12.8	67.1	55.0	71	2.8	13	6.83	—	—
Aug.	19.5	12.9	67.1	55.2	83	3.3	15	6.42	—	—
Sept.	17.9	11.9	64.2	53.4	91	3.6	15	5.24	—	0.3
Oct.	15.3	9.9	59.5	49.8	101	4.0	16	3.68	—	1.6
Nov.	12.1	6.9	53.8	44.4	128	5.0	24	2.51	0.9	6.8
Dec.	10.4	5.6	50.7	42.1	130	5.1	21	1.89	2.9	9.4
Extremes	29.4	−8.3	84.9	17.0	—	—	—	—	—	—
Year	14.2	8.4	57.6	52.3	1098	43.3	206	1719.9	14.8	58.8

Plymouth (Mount Batten)   Height: 27m (86.6ft)

	Average temperatures				Average rainfall		Average sunshine	Average number of days frost	
	Centigrade		Fahrenheit						
					Per month		Days per month	Hours per day	Air	Ground
	Max.	Min.	Max.	Min.	mm	in				
Jan.	8.0	3.8	46.4	38.8	108	4.3	18	1.81	6.6	11.7
Feb.	7.9	3.2	46.2	37.8	75	3.0	14	2.83	6.6	11.9
Mar.	9.9	4.3	49.8	39.7	74	2.9	14	4.27	4.6	12.2
April	12.3	6.1	54.1	43.0	57	2.2	17	6.10	0.7	5.6
May	14.9	8.2	58.8	46.8	68	2.7	15	7.11	—	1.5
June	17.6	11.1	63.7	52.0	56	2.2	11	7.43	—	0.1
July	19.0	12.7	66.2	54.9	70	2.8	12	6.67	—	—
Aug	19.0	12.7	66.2	54.9	85	3.4	15	6.18	—	—
Sept.	17.5	11.6	63.5	52.9	86	3.4	15	5.00	—	0.3
Oct.	14.8	9.4	58.6	48.9	92	3.6	15	3.63	—	2.3
Nov.	11.1	6.4	52.0	43.5	109	4.3	19	2.27	1.8	7.6
Dec.	9.2	4.9	48.6	40.8	110	4.3	19	1.73	6.4	12.5
Extremes	31.1	−8.9	88.0	16.0	—	—	—	—	—	—
Year	13.4	7.9	56.1	46.2	990	39.1	184	1677.8	26.7	65.7

Princetown (Dartmoor)   Height: 414m (1,358.3ft)

	Average temperatures				Average rainfall		Average sunshine		Average number of days frost	
	Centigrade		Fahrenheit							
					Per month		Days per month	Hours per day	Air	Ground
	Max.	Min.	Max.	Min.	mm	in				
Jan.	5.1	0.5	41.2	32.9	211	8.3	22		13.4	18.1
Feb.	4.8	0.1	40.6	32.2	144	5.7	18		13.2	17.7
Mar.	7.4	1.3	45.3	34.3	142	5.6	17		6.0	13.4
April	10.2	3.5	50.4	38.3	117	4.6	14		2.4	9.4
May	13.0	5.8	55.4	42.4	126	5.0	15		—	0.5
June	15.9	8.9	60.6	48.0	112	4.4	16		—	0.3
July	17.1	10.4	62.8	50.7	138	5.4	17	No	—	0.1
Aug.	16.9	10.6	62.4	51.1	160	6.3	19	Record	—	—
Sept.	14.9	9.2	58.8	48.6	171	6.7	19		—	0.3
Oct.	12.0	6.9	53.6	44.4	173	6.8	18		0.4	3.1
Nov.	8.1	3.6	56.6	38.5	211	8.3	21		2.4	9.5
Dec.	6.2	1.8	43.2	35.2	219	8.6	23		6.8	13.8
Extremes	30.0	−13.3	86.0	8.1	—	—	—		—	—
Year	11.0	5.2	51.8	41.4	1924	75.7	219		44.6	86.2

St Mary's, Scilly

Height: 48m (157.5ft)

| | Average temperatures | | | | Average rainfall | | Average sunshine | | Average number of days frost | |
| | Centigrade | | Fahrenheit | | | | | | | |
	Max.	Min.	Max.	Min.	Per month mm	in	Days per month	Hours per day	Air	Ground
Jan.	9.1	6.2	48.4	43.2	92	3.6	21	1.93	1.2	
Feb.	8.9	5.6	48	42.1	77	3.0	17	2.85	0.2	
Mar.	10.5	6.5	50.9	43.7	69	2.7	17	4.26	0.5	
April	12.2	7.5	54	45.5	47	1.9	16	6.34	—	
May	14.4	9.3	57.9	48.7	65	2.6	17	7.58	—	
June	17.1	11.7	62.8	53.1	49	1.9	14	7.45	—	
July	18.7	13.3	65.7	55.9	62	2.4	11	6.72	—	No
Aug.	19.0	13.6	66.2	56.5	71	2.8	15	6.53	—	Record
Sept.	17.5	12.8	63.5	55	72	2.8	14	5.14	—	
Oct.	14.9	11.0	58.8	51.8	78	3.1	15	3.73	—	
Nov.	11.8	8.6	53.2	47.5	99	3.9	21	2.50	—	
Dec.	10.1	7.3	50.2	45.1	100	3.9	20	1.86	0.1	
Extremes	27.8	−5.0	82	23	—	—	—	—	—	
Year	13.7	9.5	56.7	49.1	881	34.6	198	1734.6	2.0	

St Mawgan

Height: 103m (337.9ft)

| | Average temperatures | | | | Average rainfall | | Average sunshine | | Average number of days frost | |
| | Centigrade | | Fahrenheit | | Per month | | Days per month | Hours per day | Air | Ground |
	Max.	Min.	Max.	Min.	mm	in				
Jan.	8.1	3.8	46.6	38.8	109	4.3	20	1.99	6.2	8.3
Feb.	7.6	2.8	45.7	37.0	76	3.0	15	2.97	7.1	9.9
Mar.	9.7	4.2	49.5	39.6	71	2.8	16	4.35	3.9	6.5
April	11.9	5.8	53.4	42.4	57	2.2	15	6.36	0.7	3.8
May	14.3	8.0	57.7	46.4	71	2.8	14	7.07	—	0.3
June	17.1	10.9	62.8	51.6	55	2.2	13	7.28	—	0.1
July	18.3	12.6	64.9	54.7	75	2.3	14	6.40	—	—
Aug.	18.5	12.6	65.3	54.7	84	3.3	17	6.13	—	—
Sept.	17.2	11.6	63	52.9	86	3.4	16	5.00	—	0.1
Oct.	14.3	9.4	57.7	48.9	95	3.7	17	3.58	—	0.3
Nov.	10.8	6.3	51.4	43.3	114	4.5	20	2.52	0.9	4.0
Dec.	8.8	4.9	47.8	40.8	119	4.7	21	1.86	4.7	8.1
Extremes	30.6	−10.0	87.1	14	—	—	—	—	—	—
Year	13.0	7.7	55.4	45.9	1012	39.2	198	1690.9	23.5	41.4

Torbay

Height: 8m (26.2ft)

	Average temperatures				Average rainfall		Average sunshine	Average number of days frost		
	Centigrade		Fahrenheit							
					Per month		Days per month	Hours per day	Air	Ground
	Max.	Min.	Max.	Min.	mm	in				
Jan.	8.4	3.0	47.1	37.4	103	4.1	17	1.93	6.6	10.7
Feb.	8.3	2.9	46.9	37.2	72	2.8	13	2.91	6.4	10.3
Mar.	10.2	4.1	50.4	39.4	70	2.8	13	4.33	4.1	9.1
April	13.1	6.0	55.6	42.8	52	2.1	15	6.33	0.7	3.1
May	15.5	8.3	59.9	46.9	69	2.7	14	7.29	—	0.3
June	18.6	11.4	65.5	52.5	46	1.8	10	7.87	—	—
July	20.0	13.0	68	55.4	57	2.2	11	7.16	—	—
Aug.	19.9	13.0	67.8	55.4	70	2.8	13	6.56	—	—
Sept.	18.1	11.7	65.6	21.1	75	3.0	13	5.16	—	—
Oct.	15.2	9.2	59.4	48.6	83	3.3	14	3.72	—	0.6
Nov.	11.5	5.8	52.7	42.4	102	4.0	17	2.46	1.3	5.9
Dec.	9.6	4.1	59.3	39.4	99	3.9	17	2.03	5.8	9.9
Extremes	30.6	−8.9	87.1	16	—	—	—	—	—	—
Year	14.0	7.7	57.2	45.9	898	35.5	167	1760.1	24.9	49.9

Weymouth

Height: 5m (16.4ft)

	Average temperatures				Average rainfall			Average sunshine	Average number of days frost	
	Centigrade		Fahrenheit							
					Per month		Days per month	Hours per day	Air	Ground
	Max.	Min.	Max.	Min.	mm	in				
Jan.	7.9	2.8	46.2	37.0	85	3.4	17	2.05	8.5	
Feb.	8.0	2.5	46.4	36.5	57	2.2	12	2.96	8.4	
Mar.	10.2	3.7	50.4	38.7	56	2.2	13	4.42	4.5	
April	13.3	5.8	55.9	42.4	46	1.8	13	6.35	1.3	
May	16.1	8.2	61.0	46.8	56	2.2	14	7.35	0.1	
June	18.9	11.2	66.0	52.2	44	1.7	10	7.90	—	
July	20.3	13.1	68.5	55.6	55	2.2	8	7.30	—	No
Aug	20.4	13.2	68.7	55.8	68	2.7	10	6.67	—	Record
Sept.	18.6	11.9	55.5	53.4	77	3.0	10	5.20	—	
Oct.	15.6	9.3	60.1	48.7	79	3.1	13	3.95	0.2	
Nov.	11.4	5.9	52.5	42.6	95	3.7	17	2.53	2.5	
Dec.	9.2	3.9	48.6	39.0	87	3.4	15	2.01	6.4	
Extremes	32.2	−9.5	90.0	14.9	—	—	—	—	—	
Year	14.1	7.7	57.4	45.9	805	31.6	152	1789.4	31.9	

References

BBC. *Spotlight South West* programme scripts 1968, 1976, 1978 and 1979

Bowen, David. *Britain's Weather* (David & Charles, 1973)

Gill, Crispin. *Dartmoor* (David & Charles, 1976)

Keesing's Contemporary Archives Weekly Diary of World Events 1952—1954, p.12434

Lamb, H.H. *The English Climate* (English Universities Press, London, 1964)

Marshall, W.A.L. 'The Lynmouth Floods', *Weather*, Vol.7, No.11 (November 1952)

Millward, Roy and Robinson, Adrian. *The South West Peninsula* (Macmillan, 1971)

Doorway to Devon (Devon County Council, 1977)

Plymouth (Plymouth Marketing Bureau, 1980)

Properties Open 1978 (The National Trust, 1978)

The West Country and other brochures. (West Country Tourist Board, 1980)

Acknowledgements

I am indebted to:
The United Kingdom Meteorological Office, London Road, Bracknell, Berkshire for providing me with climatological data on which the tables in the Appendix are based; Peter Chester, Director, West Country Tourist Board and Gerald Ferguson, National Secretary, The Surf Life Saving Association of Great Britain, for valuable information; and Steve Daniel of Steve Daniel Marine Sports, Plymouth, for his advice on surfing.

Craig Rich,
Hartley, Plymouth
January 1980

British Library Cataloguing in Publication Data

Rich, Craig Anthony
    Spotlight South West's West Country weather
    guide.
    1. West Country, Eng. – Climate
  I. Title
  551.6'9'423   QC989.G72W/

    ISBN 0-7153-8052-4

© Peninsular Books 1980

Photoset by Photo-Graphics, Honiton Devon
and printed in Great Britain
by Redwood Burn Ltd, Trowbridge, Wilts.
for David & Charles (Publishers) Limited
Brunel House Newton Abbot Devon